First published by Affirm Press, 2021
28 Thistlethwaite Street, South Melbourne,
Boon Wurrung Country, VIC 3205
affirmpress.com.au
10 9 8 7 6 5 4 3 2 1

Text copyright © Emmaline Carroll Southwell, 2021
Illustrations copyright © Vivian Mineker, 2021

 A catalogue record for this
book is available from the
National Library of Australia

ISBN: 9781922419293 (hardback)
Cover and internal design by Mika Tabata © Affirm Press
Printed and bound in China by RR Donnelley Asia Printing Solutions Ltd.

Our Family Pledge

EMMALINE CARROLL SOUTHWELL

VIVIAN MINEKER

Affirm
press

a story that we tell.
rage,

These words are actions that we practice throughout the day,
for ourselves, each other, and the planet,
and these are the words we say ...

If you look or sound different,
    if you're trans or gay,
        I love and respect you every single day.

If your beliefs are different, I accept and let be.
As long as we're kind, there's space for you and for me.

We don't all have to be best friends, that is A-OK.
I can still show respect before I walk away.

I speak up for what is right, there is power in my voice.
I step in when people need me, watching on is not my choice.

If I need help I will ask, that's the brave thing to do.

And if I do something wrong,
I'll apologise to you.

The earth is my home,
 I take care of it the best.

I leave it in good condition,
            for I am just a guest.

I nurture my soul, my body, and my mind.
I don't need to be perfect, to myself I am kind.

If I'm ever in doubt of how to proceed,
I follow my instincts, they're the path that I lead.

I'll forever work hard,
explore, learn and play.

There's no 'life blueprint' but I do these each day.

When I fail, it might hurt,
but I push on and try.

I must learn to fall if I ever want to fly.

And when I feel alone or sad,
                I hug myself so tight.

I treasure who I am,
I let this love shine bright.

This is our family pledge, a story we give to you.
Allow it to evolve, so to you it's always true.

And let's try to make this world a better place to be.

A place where we can all feel happier and free.

Loving thoughts, loving words,
loving heart on this day.

I am safe, I am loved,
life is great, hip hip oh yay!